football earth

The Wild Side

A Cartoon Collection of Footballing Animals

Steve English

THE WILD SIDE

Summersdale Publishers Ltd
46 West Street
Chichester
West Sussex
PO19 1RP
UK

www.summersdale.com

Printed and bound in China

ISBN: 978-1-84953-979-1

Substantial discounts on bulk quantities of Summersdale books are available to corporations, professional associations and other organisations. For details contact Nicky Douglas by telephone: +44 (0) 1243 756902, fax: +44 (0) 1243 786300 or email: nicky@summersdale.com.

For Amy and Joe

SHIRTS V. SKINS

Penguins use their feet to keep their eggs off the cold ice.

The moths were having a good game until the floodlights went on.

JUMPERS FOR GOALPOSTS

THE OFFSIDE TRAP

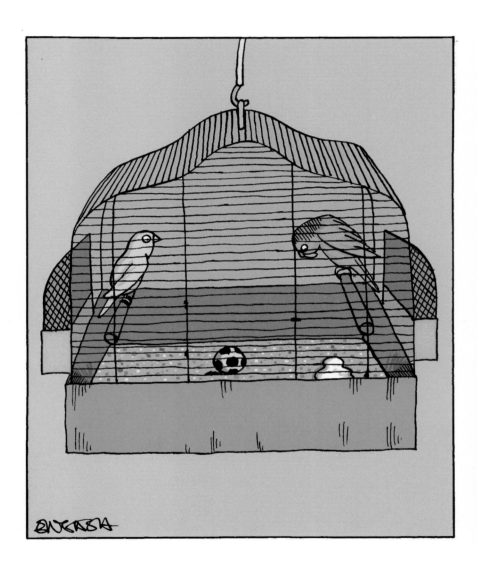

Budgie was
disappointed
that he hadn't
actually kept a
clean sheet.

Swifts spend most of their life on the wing.

The team could never rely on their No.9.

LEGENDS OF THE NATURAL GAME

Mum and Dad decided not to tell Junior what leather was made of.

FOOTBALLERS' MATES

Though the team won the tournament they had to go inside for the celebrations.

It was a dead ball situation.

It was the
end of a
short career,
but it was a
glorious save!

THE TECHNICAL AREA

It was No.7's job to take care of the seagull midfield.

Though the mix-up was quickly spotted, Hammy never ran the line again.

He was considered their greatest holding midfielder.

THE FOUR–THREE–TWO–ONE FORMATION

PENALTY PRACTICE

Their new
manager was a
free-range
chicken.

In olden days, pig bladders were used as footballs.

A shortage of funds didn't stop the manager and his chief scout shopping for new players.

The new signing
was said to be
technically very
good, but his
teammates were
not convinced.

The match ball arrives.

The manager decided to build the team around his top striker.

A TOUR OF THE NEW STADIUM

His career came to a premature end when long shorts
came into the game.

A RISKY BID FOR A NEW STRIKER

The manager's quiet, steely gaze was usually enough to command the respect of the team.

The youth coach reveals his plans for the team's
crop of new players.

He would go on to miss the shot, but it was a historic moment in the story of evolution.

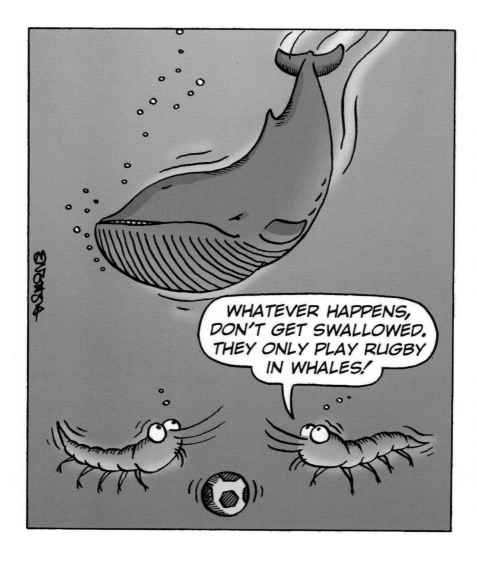

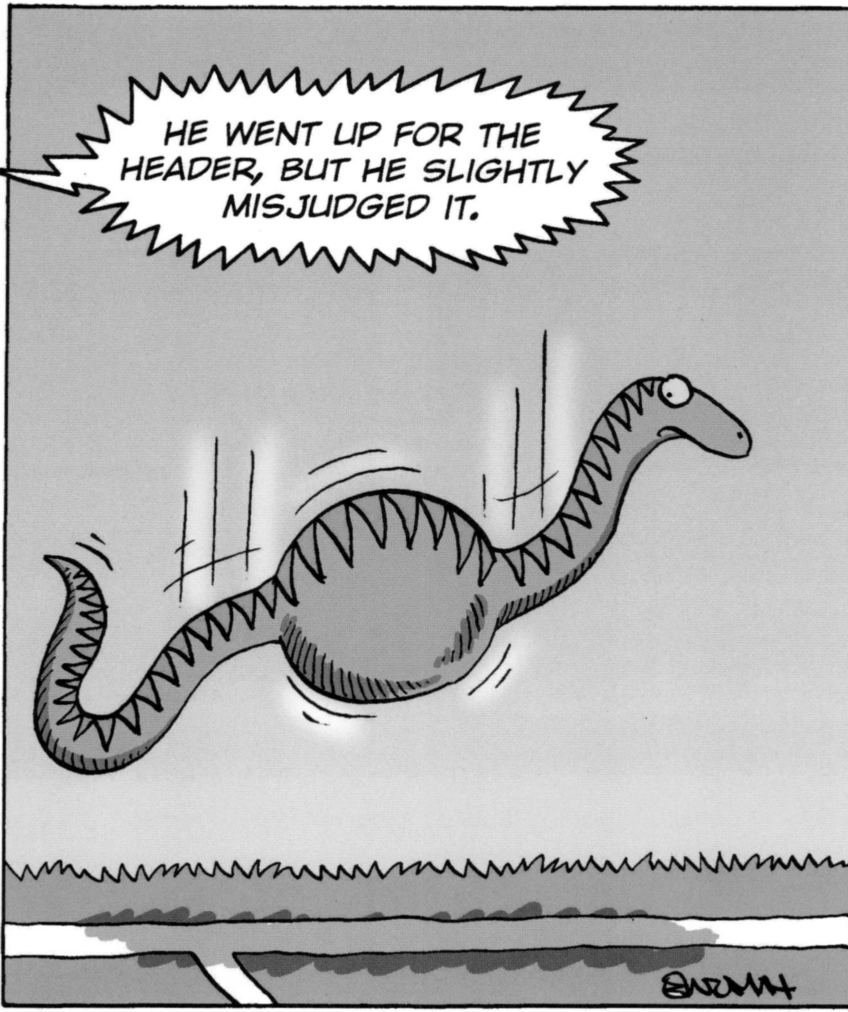
HE WENT UP FOR THE HEADER, BUT HE SLIGHTLY MISJUDGED IT.

While the cat's away…

KEEPY PUPPIES

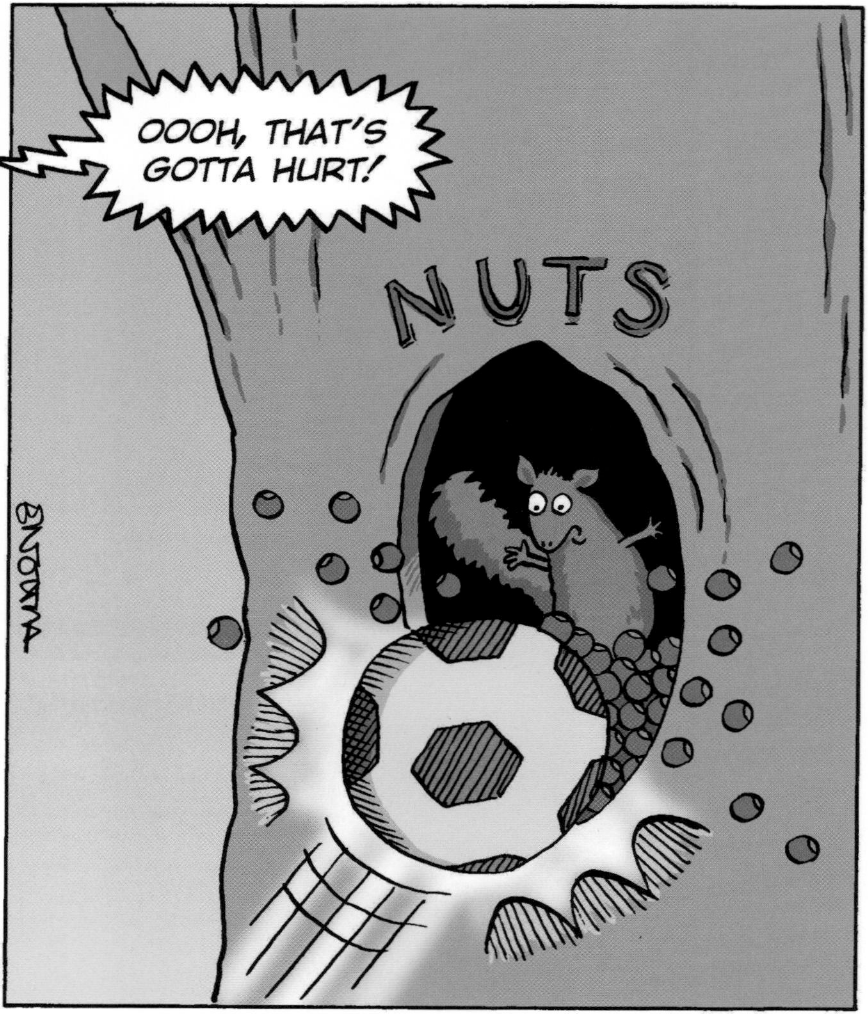
OOOH, THAT'S GOTTA HURT!
NUTS

One of life's questions answered.

How the big star players like to spend their money.

Champion's new job wasn't as exciting as he had expected it to be.

The club had
a reputation
for producing
hard players.

No one saw the incident, but later it was diagnosed as a hamstring injury.

As the No.5 approached the empty net he didn't realise that it was also approaching him.

CONFUSION OVER HALF-TIME REFRESHMENTS

The team were well known for their man-marking.

Many thought her career was over, but she was a survivor.

She wished she
hadn't started
playing with
her hair.

At half-time the team knew they were in for a real roasting.

The match came to an abrupt end when the groundsman
switched the wrong lights on.

It wasn't hard to send the keeper the wrong way.

The team were a little unsure about the new manager's backroom staff.

After the match, discussion raged over whether or not the keeper had left his box.

The new hawk-eye technology was not popular with keepers.

The noises coming out of the boardroom were not positive.

He had indeed left a foot in, but the good news was that
it would grow back.

The new manager had great things to say, but they had
to be under 140 characters.

Football was played at the dawn of time, but there was very little coverage.

It was only then
that he realised
the mascot was not
a complimentary
pre-match snack.

The moment the team's new signing put his boots on,
they knew they had made a mistake.

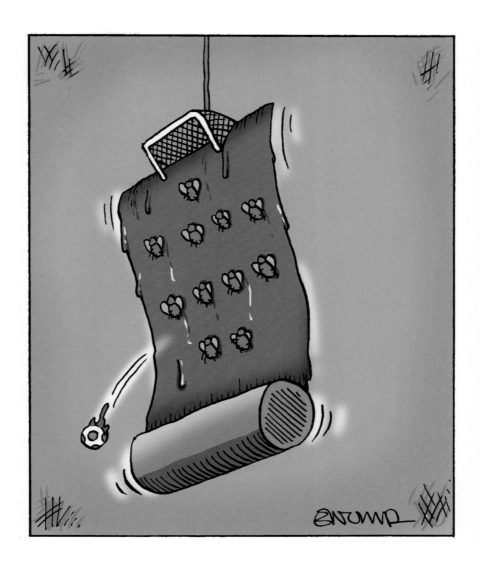

The team looked good on paper, but when it came to the match
they were pretty useless.

He never did get over the spitting incident.

It was one of life's great joys to be able to take his son
to the match.

The players always hated getting a new sponsor.

It wasn't until half-time that the manager realised he was wearing his right-back.

The manager really had lost the dressing room.

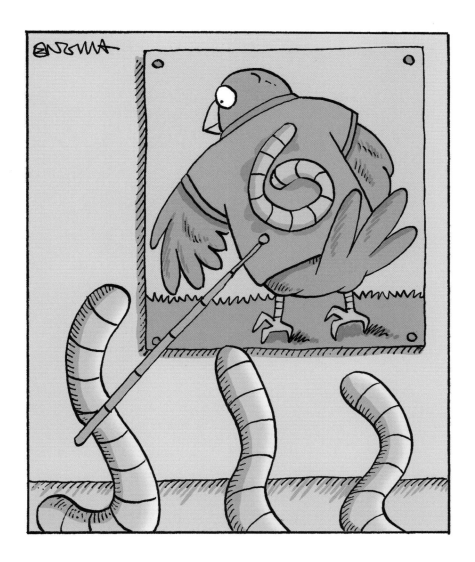

It was then that the team realised they were in the competition to make up the numbers.

The team had a disastrous cup draw.

So far the wall was
doing its job, but
it only took one to
get through.

If you're interested in finding out more about our books, find us on Facebook at **Summersdale Publishers** and follow us on Twitter at **@Summersdale**.

www.summersdale.com